What's New?

We learn about our world through new experiences.

SCHOLASTIC

LITERACY PLACE (R)

Copyright acknowledgments and credits appear on page 120, which constitutes an extension of this copyright page.

Copyright © 1996 by Scholastic Inc.   All rights reserved.   Printed in the U.S.A.
                                             ISBN 0-590-48655-1

                    5 6 7 8 9 10   24   02 01 00 99 98 97 96

Have Fun

at a Wilderness School

We learn about our world through new experiences.

New Places, New Faces

New experiences are part of everyone's life.

The More I Know, The More I Grow

We're learning new things all the time.

Dear Jim,
How's your summer going? Mine's great so far. Camp is cool. There's a lake
July 20

I Can Do It

We can meet new challenges.

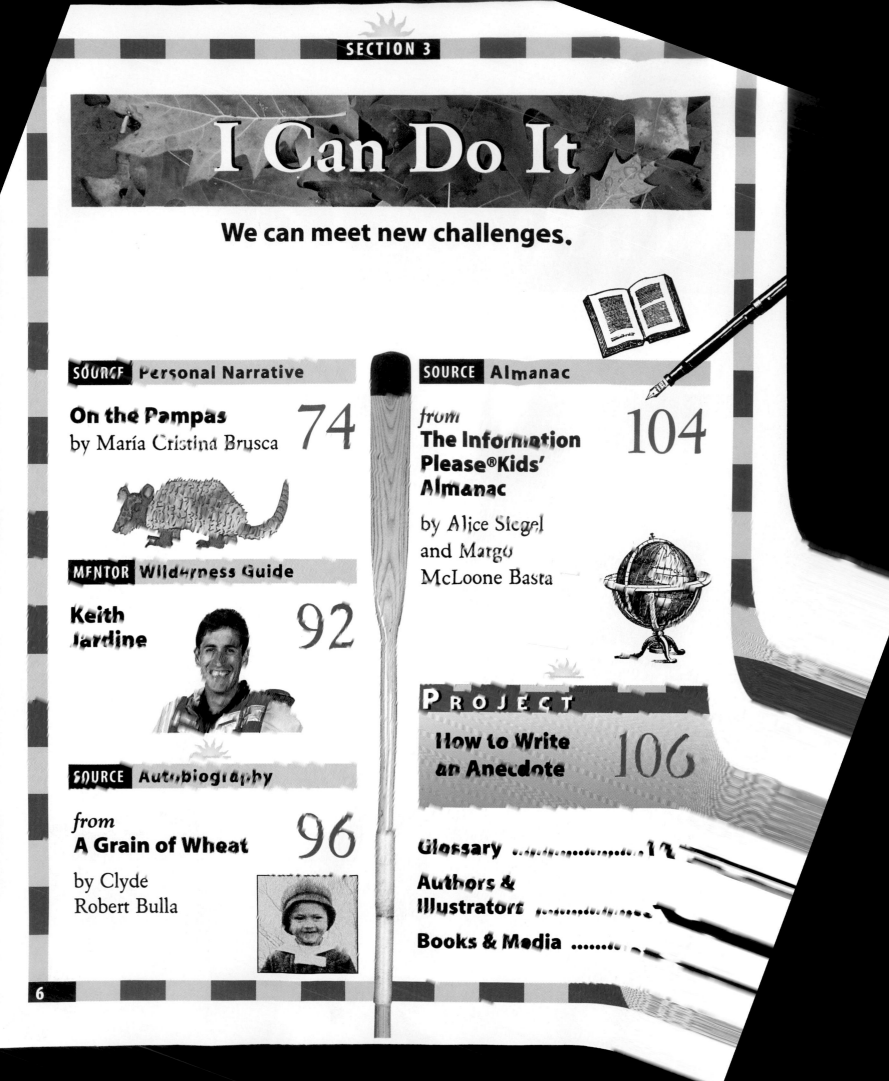

Trade Books

The following
books accompany this
What's New?
SourceBook.

Realistic Fiction

AWARD
WINNING
Book

The Chalk Box Kid

by Clyde
Robert Bulla
illustrated by
Thomas B. Allen

Historical Fiction

AWARD
WINNING
Book

Hannah

by Gloria Whelan
illustrated by
Leslie Bowman

Realistic Fiction

AWARD
WINNING
Book

Muggie Maggie

by Beverly
Cleary
illustrated by
Kay Life

Historical Fiction

AWARD
WINNING
Book

Uncle Jed's Barbershop

by Margaree
King Mitchell
illustrated by
James Ransome

New Places, New Faces

Discover what it's like to move to a new place—Gila monster country.

Explore what poets say about different kinds of changes.

Learn how Ramona Quimby feels about a new baby sister.

WORKSHOP 1

Make a chart about some of the milestones in your life.

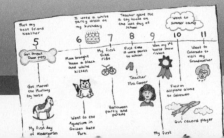

9

Gila monsters meet you at the airport

by Marjorie Weinman Sharmat
illustrated by Byron Barton

«1»

I live at 165 East 95th Street, New York City,
and I'm going to stay here forever.

My mother and father are moving. Out West.

They say I have to go, too.
They say I can't stay here forever.

Out West nobody plays baseball because they're
too busy chasing buffaloes.

And there's cactus everywhere you look.
But if you don't look, you have to stand up
just as soon as you sit down.

Out West it takes fifteen minutes just to say hello.
Like this: H-O-W-W-W-D-Y, P-A-A-A-R-D-N-E-R.

Out West I'll look silly all the time. I'll have to wear
chaps and spurs and a bandanna and a hat so big that
nobody can find me underneath it. And I'll have to ride
a horse to school every day and I don't know how.

Out West everybody grows up to be a sheriff.
I want to be a subway driver.

My best friend is Seymour, and we like to eat
salami sandwiches together.

Out West I probably won't have any friends,
but if I do, they'll be named Tex or Slim,
and we'll eat chili and beans for breakfast. And lunch.
And dinner. While I miss Seymour and salami.

I'm on my way. Out West. It's cool in the airplane.

The desert is so hot you can collapse, and then
the buzzards circle overhead, but no one rescues
you because it's real life and not the movies.
There are clouds out the window.
No buzzards yet.

I'm looking at a map. Before, whenever I looked
at a map, I always knew my house was on the right.
But no more.
Now I'm in the middle of that map,
and I'm going left, left. Out West.

Seymour says there are Gila monsters and
horned toads out West, and I read it in a
book so I know it's so.
But Seymour says they meet you at the airport.

« 3 »

We're here.

Out West.

I don't know what a Gila monster or horned toad looks like, but I don't think I see any at the airport.

I see a boy in a cowboy hat.

He looks like Seymour, but I know his name is Tex.

"Hi," I say.

"Hi," he says. "I'm moving East."

"Great!" I say.

"*Great?*" he says. "What's so great about it? Don't you know that the streets are full of gangsters? They all wear flowers in their lapels so they look honest, but they zoom around in big cars with screeching brakes. You have to jump out of their way.

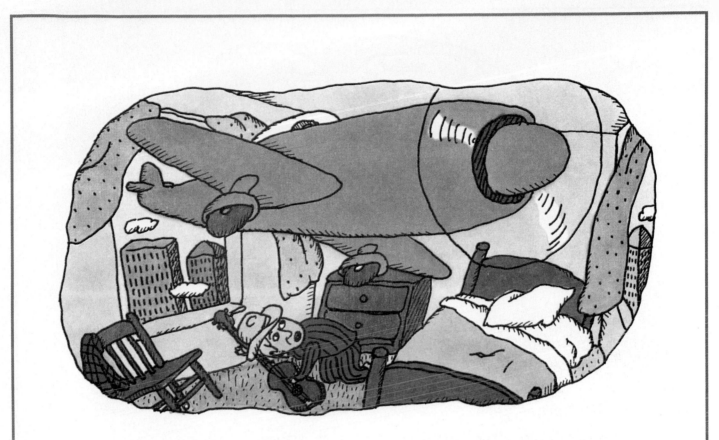

"In the East it snows and blows all the time,
except for five minutes when it's spring and summer.

"And you have to live on the 50th floor. Airplanes fly
through your bedroom, and you've got to duck fast.

"They ran out of extra space in the East a long time
ago. It's so crowded people sit on top of each other
when they ride to work.

"And alligators live in the sewers. I read it in a book
so I know it's so."

Then the mother and father of the boy who looks like
Seymour but isn't grab his hand, and he goes off.
"Sometimes the alligators get out," he yells to me.
"And they wait for you at the airport."

« 4 »

It's warm, but there's a nice breeze.
We're in a taxi riding to our new house.

No horses yet.
I don't see any buffalo stampedes either.

I see a restaurant just like the one in my old
neighborhood.

I see some kids playing baseball.

I see a horse. Hey, that's a great-looking horse!
I'm going to ask my mother and father for one like it.

Here's our house.
Some kids are riding their bikes in front of it.
I hope one of them is named Slim.

Tomorrow I'm writing a long letter to Seymour.
I'll tell him I'm sending it by pony express.
Seymour will believe me.
Back East they don't know much about us Westerners.

Always Changing

from
YELLOW BUTTER PURPLE JELLY
RED JAM BLACK BREAD

A Year Later

by Mary Ann Hoberman

Last summer I couldn't swim at all;
I couldn't even float!
I had to use a rubber tube
Or hang on to a boat;
I had to sit on shore
While everybody swam.
But now it's this summer
And I can.

from
THE BUTTERFLY JAR

Moving

by Jeff Moss

Mom and Dad told us we're moving
To a better city
With a nicer house
And a better school
With great new friends
And even the weather will be sunnier.

What I want to know is
If everything's so great where we're moving
How come we didn't decide to live there in the first place?

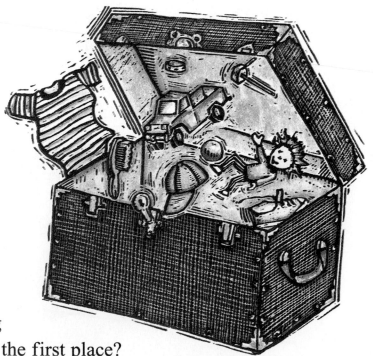

20

from
BRONZEVILLE BOYS AND GIRLS

Narcissa

by Gwendolyn Brooks

Some of the girls are playing jacks.
Some are playing ball.
But small Narcissa is not playing
Anything at all.

Small Narcissa sits upon
A brick in her back yard
And looks at tiger-lilies,
And shakes her pigtails hard.

First she is an ancient queen
In pomp and purple veil.
Soon she is a singing wind.
And, next, a nightingale.

How fine to be Narcissa,
A-changing like all that!
While sitting still, as still, as still
As anyone ever sat!

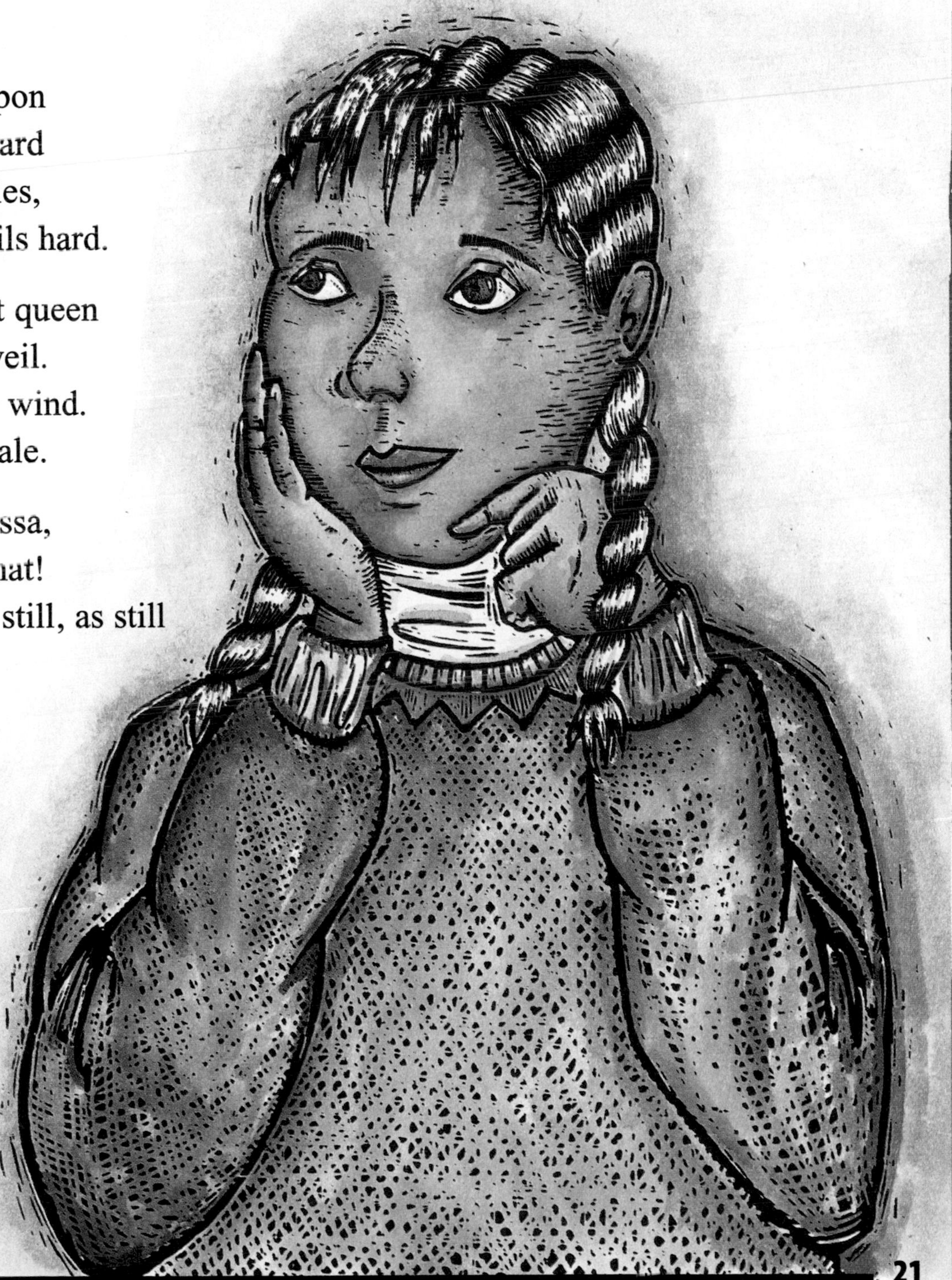

from

Ramona FOREVER

by **Beverly Cleary**

illustrated by **Alan Tiegreen**

AWARD WINNING

Book

It's an exciting time for the Quimby family!
Ramona's mother has just had a beautiful baby girl.
Visiting her mother and baby Roberta at the hospital
will be a real thrill, but Ramona is also worried. A
baby around the house could change everything.

The day was long and lonely. Even a swimming
lesson at the park and a trip to the library did little to
make time pass. "I wonder what Roberta looks like?"
said Beezus.

"And whose room she will share when she outgrows
the bassinette?" worried Ramona.

The one happy moment in the day for the girls was a telephone call from their mother, who reported that Roberta was a beautiful, healthy little sister. She couldn't wait to bring her home, and she was proud of her daughters for being so good about staying alone. This pleased Beezus and Ramona so much they ran the vacuum cleaner and dusted, which made time pass faster until their father, looking exhausted, came home to take them out for hamburgers and a visit to the fifth Quimby.

Ramona could feel her heart pounding as she finally climbed the steps to the hospital. Visitors, some carrying flowers and the others looking careworn, walked toward the elevators. Nurses hurried, a doctor was paged over the loudspeaker. Ramona could scarcely bear her own excitement. The rising of the elevator made her stomach feel as if it had stayed behind on the first floor. When the elevator stopped, Mr. Quimby led the way down the hall.

"Excuse me," called a nurse. Surprised, the family stopped and turned.

"Children under twelve are not allowed to visit the maternity ward," said the nurse. "Little girl, you will have to go down and wait in the lobby."

"Why is that?" asked Mr. Quimby.

"Children under twelve might have contagious diseases," explained the nurse. "We have to protect the babies."

"I'm sorry, Ramona," said Mr. Quimby. "I didn't know. I am afraid you will have to do as the nurse says."

"Does she mean I'm *germy*?" Ramona was humiliated. "I took a shower this morning and washed my hands at the Whopperburger so I would be extra clean."

"Sometimes children are coming down with something and don't know it," explained Mr. Quimby. "Now, be a big girl and go downstairs and wait for us."

Ramona's eyes filled with tears of disappointment, but she found some pleasure in riding in the elevator alone. By the time she reached the lobby, she felt worse. The nurse called her a little girl. Her father called her a big girl. What was she? A germy girl.

Ramona sat gingerly on the edge of a Naugahyde couch. If she leaned back, she might get germs on it, or it might get germs on her. She swallowed hard. Was her throat a little bit sore? She thought maybe it was, way down in back. She put her hand to her forehead the way her mother did when she thought Ramona might have a fever. Her forehead was warm, maybe too warm.

As Ramona waited, she began to itch the way she itched when she had chickenpox. Her head itched, her back itched, her legs itched. Ramona scratched. A woman sat down on the couch, looked at Ramona, got up, and moved to another couch.

Ramona felt worse. She itched **more** and scratched harder. She **swallowed** often to see how her **sore throat** was coming along. **She peeked** down the neck of her **blouse to see** if she might have a **rash and was** surprised that she did **not. She** sniffed from time to time **to see if she** had a runny nose.

Now Ramona was angry. It would serve everybody right if she came down with some horrible disease, right there in their old hospital. That would show everybody how germfree the place was. Ramona squirmed and gave that hard-to-reach place between her shoulder blades a good hard scratch. Then she scratched her head with both hands. People stopped to stare.

A man in a white coat, with a stethoscope hanging out of his pocket, came hurrying through the lobby, glanced at Ramona, stopped, and took a good look at her. "How do you feel?" he asked.

"Awful," she admitted. "A nurse said I was too germy to go see my mother and new sister, but I think I caught some disease right here."

"I see," said the doctor. "Open your mouth and say 'ah'."

Ramona *ahhed* until she gagged.

"Mh-hm," murmured the doctor. He looked so serious Ramona was alarmed. Then he pulled out his stethoscope and listened to her front and back, thumping as he did so. What was he hearing? Was there something wrong with her insides? Why didn't her father come?

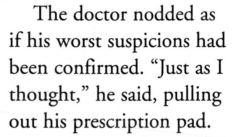

The doctor nodded as if his worst suspicions had been confirmed. "Just as I thought," he said, pulling out his prescription pad.

Medicine, ugh. Ramona's twitching stopped. Her nose and throat felt fine. "I feel much better," she assured the doctor as she eyed that prescription pad with distrust.

"An acute case of siblingitis. Not at all unusual around here, but it shouldn't last long." He tore off the prescription he had written, instructed Ramona to give it to her father, and hurried on down the hall.

Ramona could not remember the name of her illness. She tried to read the doctor's scribbly cursive writing, but she could not. She could only read neat cursive, the sort her teacher wrote on the blackboard.

Itching again, she was still staring at the slip of paper when Mr. Quimby and Beezus stepped out of the elevator. "Roberta is so tiny." Beezus was radiant with joy. "And she is perfectly darling. She has a little round nose and—oh, when you see her, you'll love her."

"I'm sick." Ramona tried to sound pitiful. "I've got something awful. A doctor said so."

Beezus paid no attention. "And Roberta has brown hair—"

Mr. Quimby interrupted. "What's this all about, Ramona?"

"A doctor said I had something, some kind of *itis*, and I have to have this right away." She handed her father the prescription and scratched one shoulder. "If I don't, I might get sicker."

Mr. Quimby read the scribbly cursive, and then he did a strange thing. He lifted Ramona and gave her a big hug and a kiss, right there in the lobby. The itching stopped. Ramona felt much better. "You have acute siblingitis," explained her father. "*Itis* means inflammation."

Ramona already knew the meaning of sibling. Since her father had studied to be a teacher, brothers and sisters had become siblings to him.

"He understood you were worried and angry because you weren't allowed to see your new sibling, and prescribed attention," explained Mr. Quimby. "Now let's all go buy ice-cream cones before I fall asleep standing up."

Beezus said Roberta was too darling to be called a dumb word like sibling. Ramona felt silly, but she also felt better.

For the next three nights, Ramona took a book to the hospital and sat in the lobby, not reading, but sulking about the injustice of having to wait to see the strange new Roberta.

On the fourth day, Mr. Quimby took an hour off from the Shop-rite Market, picked up Beezus and Ramona, who were waiting in clean clothes, and drove to the hospital to bring home his wife and new daughter.

Ramona moved closer to Beezus when she saw her mother, holding a pink bundle, emerge from the elevator in a wheelchair pushed by a nurse and followed by Mr. Quimby carrying her bag. "Can't Mother walk?" she whispered.

"Of course she can walk," answered Beezus. "The hospital wants to make sure people get out without falling down and suing for a million dollars."

Mrs. Quimby waved to the girls. Roberta's face was hidden by a corner of a pink blanket, but the nurse had no time for a little girl eager to see a new baby. She pushed the wheelchair through the automatic door to the waiting car.

"*Now* can I see her?" begged Ramona when her mother and Roberta were settled in the front, and the girls had climbed into the back seat.

"Dear Heart, of course you may." Mrs. Quimby then spoke the most beautiful words Ramona had ever heard, "Oh, Ramona, how I've missed you," as she turned back the blanket.

Ramona, leaning over the front seat for her first glimpse of the new baby sister, tried to hold her breath so she wouldn't breathe germs on Roberta, who did not look at all like the picture on the cover of *A Name for Your Baby*. Her face was bright pink, almost red, and her hair,

unlike the smooth pale hair of the baby on the cover of the pamphlet, was dark and wild. Ramona did not know what to say. She did not feel that words like darling or adorable fitted this baby.

"She looks exactly like you looked when you were born," Mrs. Quimby told Ramona.

"She does?" Ramona found this hard to believe. She could not imagine that she had once looked like this red, frowning little creature.

"Well, what do you think of your new sister?" asked Mr. Quimby.

"She's so—so *little*," Ramona answered truthfully.

Roberta opened her blue gray eyes.

"Mother!" cried Ramona. "She's cross-eyed."

Mrs. Quimby laughed. "All babies look cross-eyed sometimes. They outgrow it when they learn to focus." Sure enough, Roberta's eyes straightened out for a moment and then crossed again. She worked her mouth as if she didn't know what to do with it. She made little snuffling noises and lifted one arm as if she didn't know what it was for.

"Why does her nightie have those little pockets at the ends of the sleeves?" asked Ramona. "They cover up her hands."

"They keep her from scratching herself," explained Mrs. Quimby. "She's too little to understand that fingernails scratch."

Ramona sat back and buckled her seat belt. She had once looked like Roberta. Amazing! She had once been that tiny, but she had grown, her hair had calmed down when she remembered to comb it, and she had learned to use her eyes and hands. "You know what I think?" she asked and did not wait for an answer. "I think it is hard work to be a baby." Ramona spoke as if she had discovered something unknown to the rest of the world. With her words came unexpected love and sympathy for the tiny person in her mother's arms.

"I hadn't thought of it that way," said Mrs. Quimby, "but I think you're right."

"Growing up is hard work," said Mr. Quimby as he drove away from the hospital. "Sometimes being grown-up is hard work."

"I know," said Ramona and thought some more. She thought about loose teeth, real sore throats, quarrels, misunderstandings with her teachers, longing for a bicycle her family could not afford, worrying when her parents bickered, how terrible she had felt when she hurt Beezus's feelings without meaning to, and all the long afternoons when Mrs. Kemp looked after her until her mother came from work. She had survived it all. "Isn't it funny?" she remarked as her father steered the car into their driveway.

"Isn't what funny?" asked her mother.

"That I used to be little and funny-looking and cross-eyed like Roberta," said Ramona. "And now look at me. I'm wonderful me!"

"Except when you're blunderful you," said Beezus.

Ramona did not mind when her family, except Roberta, who was too little, laughed. "Yup, wonderful, blunderful me," she said and was happy. She was winning at growing up.

How to Make a Milestone Chart

Think of all the things you have learned and done since you were small. Each of these important events is a milestone in your life. These events can be shown on a milestone chart.

What is a milestone chart? A milestone chart lists important events. It shows the order in which each event happened.

the writer's age when the events happened

Met my best friend Heather

5

Got Great Dane puppy

Got Marvel the Mustang toy horse

My first day of Kindergarten

Teacher Mrs. Martin

chart runs from left to right

taking a fun trip

I wore a white party dress on my birthday

Teacher gave me a toy house on the last day of school

Went to summer camp

6 7 8 9 10 11

Mom brought home a black and white kitten

My first bike ride

First time I wore pants to school

Won my 1st horse show ribbon

Went to Colorado to visit my Grandmother

Went to the Aquarium in Golden Gate Park

Teacher Mrs. Cooper

Flew on airplane alone to Colorado

Got record player

My first pony

starting school

learning to do something new

getting a new pet

37

1 Which Milestones?

Make a list of some important events that have happened to you. You might begin with your first day in kindergarten. Think of things you've learned, new places you've seen, and new people in your life.

Here are some ideas: a new baby, a trip, learning to do something, moving, making a friend, or special holidays or events.

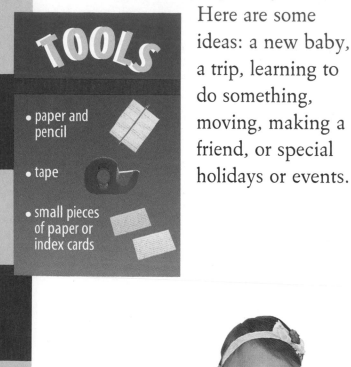

TOOLS

- paper and pencil
- tape
- small pieces of paper or index cards

2 Which Was First?

Now you need to put your milestones in order. There is an easy way to do this. Write each milestone on an index card or small piece of paper. If you know the year it happened, write that on the card, too.

Spread the cards out on a table. Put them in the order they happened. Then, number the cards so you will always know their order.

3 Make the Chart

Now it's time to make your milestone chart.

- Tape two large pieces of paper together.

- Draw a line across the paper going the long way.

- Decide if you want to make your chart run from left to right or from top to bottom.

  - Begin at the top or left side of the paper. Next to the line, write your first milestone.

Tip Use your numbered index cards to write the rest of your milestones in order. You may want to illustrate some of your milestones.

4 Show It!

Display your milestone chart on the class bulletin board. Discuss your chart with your classmates. Tell which milestones were most important to you. Look at the other charts. Do you share any of the same milestones with your classmates?

If You Are Using a Computer ...

Create your milestone chart on the computer using a program like HyperCard. Make a stack of cards about your life, with each card showing a different milestone.

THINK

Learning to do something new is one kind of milestone. What would you want to learn next?

Keith Jardine
Wilderness Guide ▶

We're learning new things all the time.

The More I Know, The More I Grow

Meet a girl who is learning to speak and write Chinese. Then find out why Native American children are studying their native languages.

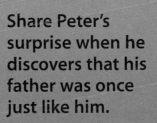

Share Peter's surprise when he discovers that his father was once just like him.

WORKSHOP 2

Write a friendly letter about an important event in your life.

CAMP SUNRISE
Dubois, WY 82900

July 20

Dear Jim,
How's your summer going? Mine's great so far. Camp is cool. There's a lake for swimming and other stuff, lots of hiking trails, and most of my ... from last year. ... day for the ...

From

How My Family Lives in America

by Susan Kuklin

My name in America is April. I also have a Chinese name: *Chin* (ching), which means "admire" and *Lan* (lan), which means "orchid."

Both my parents are Chinese and were born in Taiwan. Taiwan is an island on the other side of the world. My papa came to New York without his parents to go to school and my mama moved here with her family. Because Julius, my older brother, and May, my older sister, and I were born in America, we are called Chinese Americans.

There are many Chinese Americans. But we do not all speak the same Chinese language. The way my family speaks Chinese is called Mandarin.

欽

Admire

蘭

Orchid

Father

Mother

In Mandarin, I call my daddy *baba* (bah-bah) and my mommy *mama* (mah-mah). It sounds something like English, but when we write the words they look very different. Another thing that's different in Chinese is that words aren't made with letters. Each word has its own special marks.

During the week we go to public school, but on Saturday we go to Chinese school. There we learn how to speak and write in Chinese, like my parents learned in Taiwan. When I write English letters, I write from the left side of the page to the right. When I write in Chinese, I write from the right to the left. And I write in rows from the top of the page to the bottom. For us Chinese-American kids there are many things to remember.

In Chinese school we also learn a special kind of writing called calligraphy. We use a brush instead of a pen, black ink, and special paper made from stalks of rice. Our teacher shows us the right way to hold the brush.

芝
蔴
涼
麵

Cold Sesame
Noodles

My favorite part of Chinese school is snack time. Today, Mama made me cold sesame noodles, *tsu ma liang mein* (tsu mah leeang mee-en). I eat them with a fork, but most Chinese people eat their noodles with chopsticks. I'm just learning to eat with chopsticks.

Papa told us that an Italian explorer named Marco Polo discovered noodles in China a long time ago and introduced them to his country.

When Mama brought home takeout, Julius asked if a Chinese explorer discovered pizza in Italy.

Mama and Papa laughed and said, "No."

While we eat our pizza we play a game to test our wits. Papa asks us to look for letters hidden in the picture on the pizza box. Julius sees a *V* in the pizza man's shoe. May finds an *L*.

Oh, look! I can even see the Chinese letter *Ba* (bah), in the pizza man's eyebrows. *Ba* means "eight" in Chinese.

Eight

Chi chiao
bang

At night when we have finished all our chores and all our homework, we play *Chi chiao bang* (chee chow bang). In America some people call it Tangram. This is a popular game in Taiwan, like checkers is in America. My grandparents and even my great-grandparents played this game. To play, you move seven different shapes to build a new shape. I like to make a pussycat. It is very difficult, but I can do it. Papa says, "Go slowly and think about a cat. After a while your mind will start to run and you will see the cat in the shapes." He's right.

There is an old Chinese saying, "The older you are the wiser you become." When I become a grown-up, I will remember to tell this to my family.

April's Cold Sesame Noodles

(1 serving)

2 ounces cooked Chinese noodles or spaghetti
1 tablespoon sesame sauce or peanut butter
1 teaspoon soy sauce
1 teaspoon chopped scallion

In a bowl mix the sesame sauce (or peanut butter) with
1 tablespoon warm water and soy sauce. Add to the cooked,
cooled noodles and sprinkle scallion on top. Stir before eating.

SOURCE

SCHOLASTIC NEWS®

News Magazine

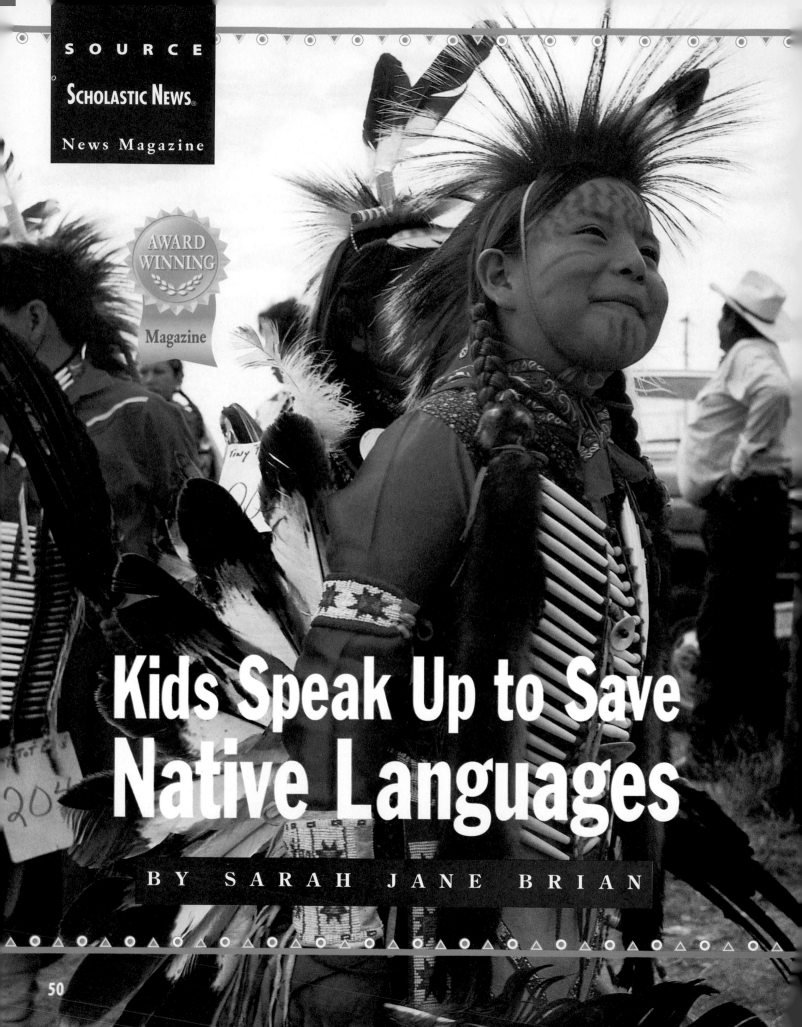

Kids Speak Up to Save Native Languages

BY SARAH JANE BRIAN

◀ Wearing colorful handmade costumes and dancing are two ways that Native Americans keep their traditions alive.

"*Hey-yung*!"

That means "hello" in the Native American language of Hupa (HOOP-ah). For thousands of years, Hupa people used this language to share their thoughts, feelings, and ideas. Today, only 20 people speak Hupa well enough to hold a conversation. All of them are older members of the tribe, called elders. Most children and young adults in the tribe speak English, and know only a few Hupa words.

▲ This Cherokee storyteller passes on traditional tales to interested listeners.

Fourth grader David Drake wants to make sure his tribe's language doesn't die out. He is one of many Hupa kids who are trying to learn Hupa before it is too late. Last summer, David and his family went to a special language camp. There, they cooked and ate traditional foods, sang songs, and listened to stories in Hupa. "It was fun," David said. "During everything that we did, we learned new words in Hupa."

◀ A young Navajo girl is learning her native language in school.

▲ During a 4th of July powwow, or get-together, these Kiowa boys and girls learn traditional dances and stories.

Lost Languages

Hupa is not the only language that is in trouble. According to expert Dr. Clay Slate, more than 1,000 different native languages were once spoken in North America. Most of them have been forgotten. Today, there are only 206 of these languages left.

In the past, the U.S. government wanted Native Americans to give up their languages. David's great-grandmother was punished when she spoke Hupa in school. Today, that has changed. In 1990, the U.S. Congress passed a law to help protect native languages. Soon, a new law may provide money for tribes that want to save their languages.

Getting Tongues Un-tied

Navajo teacher Andrew Becenti says we must save native languages because they are important parts of Native American cultures. "If you don't have the language, and you try to teach the culture, it's like food without any salt. Something's missing. It's just flat," he said.

All across the U.S., many Native Americans are already working to preserve their languages. In some places, elders work to teach younger people. On the Navajo reservation in Tuba City, Arizona, kids can take Navajo language classes in school.

Learning to speak a new language is not easy. It can take years. But people like David and his family plan to study hard for as long as it takes. "Our language is part of our heritage. We can't just let it die off," said David's mom.

WHERE AMERICAN INDIANS LIVE

Long before Columbus arrived, nearly a million people lived in America. Columbus called them Indians. They belonged to different tribes across the land. Today nearly two million American Indian people live in the U.S. states shown on this map.

Most live in towns and cities. But many live on reservations—pieces of land that have been set aside for native tribes. The large blue areas on the map show the larger reservations. The small blue areas show smaller reservations and other places where American Indians live.

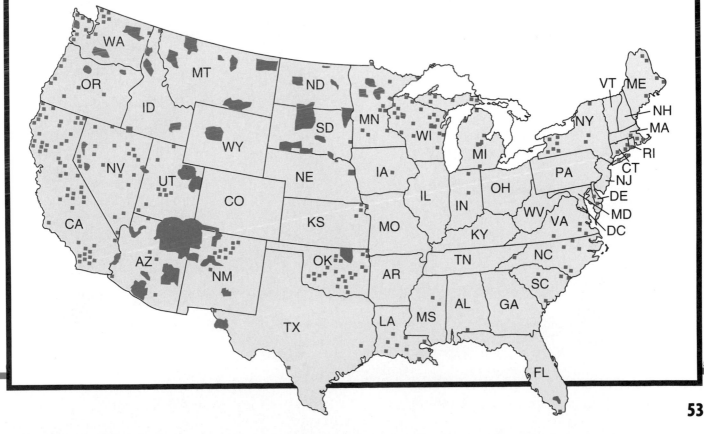

YOUR DAD WAS JUST LIKE YOU

by DOLORES JOHNSON

Peter stood at the front door of his grandfather's house. "You're the best grandpa that ever was," he said. "Can I move in with you?"

"Move in with me? What happened this time? Did you and your dad have another fight?" asked Peter's grandfather. "You two are always battlin'."

"I wasn't doin' anything, Grandpa," said Peter. "I was just playing around—you know—running, and that ole stupid purple thing on Dad's dresser just seemed to jump onto the floor and break. Dad was so mad, he didn't even yell. He was so mad, he just walked away. Grandpa, I think I need to move in with you."

"Why don't we take a walk, Grandson, and sort this problem out? Sometimes my head works better when my legs get a chance to stretch."

The two walked through the neighborhood their family had lived in for years. After they had walked some, Peter sighed, "I wish Dad was more like you, Grandpa. He never smiles—he only yells. 'Look at these awful grades, Peter.' 'You never finish anything you start, Peter.' 'Why can't you be more serious, Peter?' He just never leaves me alone."

"There was a time when your father laughed and smiled all the time," said Peter's grandfather. "When he was a boy, your dad was just like you."

"My daddy was a *boy*. . . just like *me*?" asked Peter.

"That boy would tell me silly jokes just like you tell. When I didn't even feel like smiling, that boy sure could make me laugh. All he had to do was tell his favorite knock knock jokes."

"*My* dad told *knock knock* jokes?" asked Peter. "You sure you're talking about *my* dad?"

"I know it's hard for you to believe," said his grandfather, "but when your father was young, he was like any other boy. Sometimes he played so long at this park, I almost had to drag him home. He played basketball on that court till he almost wore out the net. He even led big game safaris through that jungle gym."

"Dad played in *my* jungle?" asked Peter.

"He played combat with little green army men on the grass by those swings. He practically wore a groove in this sidewalk with his bicycle. But there was one thing that boy loved to do more than anything else in the world."

"What's that, Grandpa?" Peter chuckled. "Yell at the little kids? Start fights?"

"More than living, laughing, or eating, your father loved to run. He ran from sunup to sundown. He ran so fast that his shadow had trouble keeping up with him."

Peter asked, "So why doesn't my dad run now?"

"There came a time when he became serious. And he told himself, a serious man doesn't run."

"Did he ever run in a race?" asked Peter. "Did he ever win a prize?"

"Your father ran only one race, when he wasn't much older than you. It was the biggest race in the town for schoolkids. Your father sure wanted to win that big golden trophy."

"Dad must have lost the race, 'cause I've never seen any big golden trophy. At least not on the bookshelf where he keeps all his special stuff."

"Sometimes you don't compete for trophies just to place them high up on a shelf," said his grandfather. "Sometimes you compete so you can prove something to yourself. When your father was your age, he had something to prove. He was having trouble in school. Nothing seemed to be going right for him."

"But my daddy's so smart!" said Peter.

"He didn't think he was smart, but he *knew* he was fast. He could run like the wind, and he wanted to show everyone. He stopped playing games. He stopped laughing and joking. He ran day and night as fast as he could because he wanted to run that race and win."

"Did he win, Grandpa?"

Peter's grandfather laughed. "Are you going to let me tell my story? Everyone from town—hundreds of people—lined every inch of that one-mile course to the courthouse. About fifty boys and girls gathered at the starting line, fidgeting and milling about like pigeons on a telephone wire. The starter raised his gun. 'On your mark. . .get set. . .' he thundered. And then the worst thing that could possibly happen happened."

"What, Grandpa?"

"A drop of rain fell, and then another and another."

"It started raining?" laughed Peter. "So? I've run a million times in the rain."

"Not rain like this, boy. I looked up, and the sky had turned dark and angry. Rain poured down, and pools of water formed at my feet. The starter didn't have to say 'Go!' because the children had already started running. But they weren't running to the finish line. They were trying to find the last dry spot on earth."

"So Daddy ran for cover too, huh, Grandpa? You know, he doesn't like to mess up his clothes."

"No. It seems your father had something he just had to do. He picked up one leg after the other and ran as fast as he could toward the end of the race. And he kept running even though the rain came down so heavy it nearly knocked him down with its force. The wind howled around him, and pools of water were reaching up to drag at his feet."

"Did Daddy ever reach the finish line?"

"Yes, Grandson, but no one was there to congratulate him. No one handed him a big trophy. No one told him how good he was."

"Where were you, Grandpa?"

"I ran behind your father. I didn't catch up to him until the very end. I finally reached him as he stood alone, shaking his head and sobbing in the rain."

"So what did you do, Grandpa?"

"I picked your father up and carried him home. I dried him off and laid him down. And while he probably cried himself to sleep, I sat down with these two big, clumsy hands of mine and made my boy a trophy, because he really deserved one."

"So where is the trophy now, Grandpa?"

"Well, it . . . it was . . ." said the old man.

"Was it a big ole stupid purple . . .? Oh, I'm sorry, Grandpa. What did Dad say when you gave it to him?"

"He didn't really say much at all . . . just, 'I love you, Dad,' for the very first time. You see, when your father was a boy, he and I used to fight a lot. I used to yell at him. I hardly ever smiled. We decided to change what was wrong between us. That day, we became a real serious father and son."

"I've got to go home now, Grandpa. There's something serious I've got to do," said Peter. He hugged his grandfather tightly, and then ran the short distance home.

When Peter got home, he gathered the purple pieces that still lay in a heap in his father's bedroom. Then the boy brought them to his own bedroom and worked very hard to make what was broken whole again.

Peter stood in the doorway of the living room and watched his father read in silence. Then the little boy said just three words, even though he was so nervous he felt like running away. "Knock, knock, Dad."

His father hesitated for just a moment, looked up, smiled, and said, "Who's there?"

How to Write a Friendly Letter

People like to keep in touch with friends and relatives who live far away. One way to do this is by writing a friendly letter.

What is a friendly letter? A friendly letter is a message written to someone you know and like. In it, you can describe events in your life.

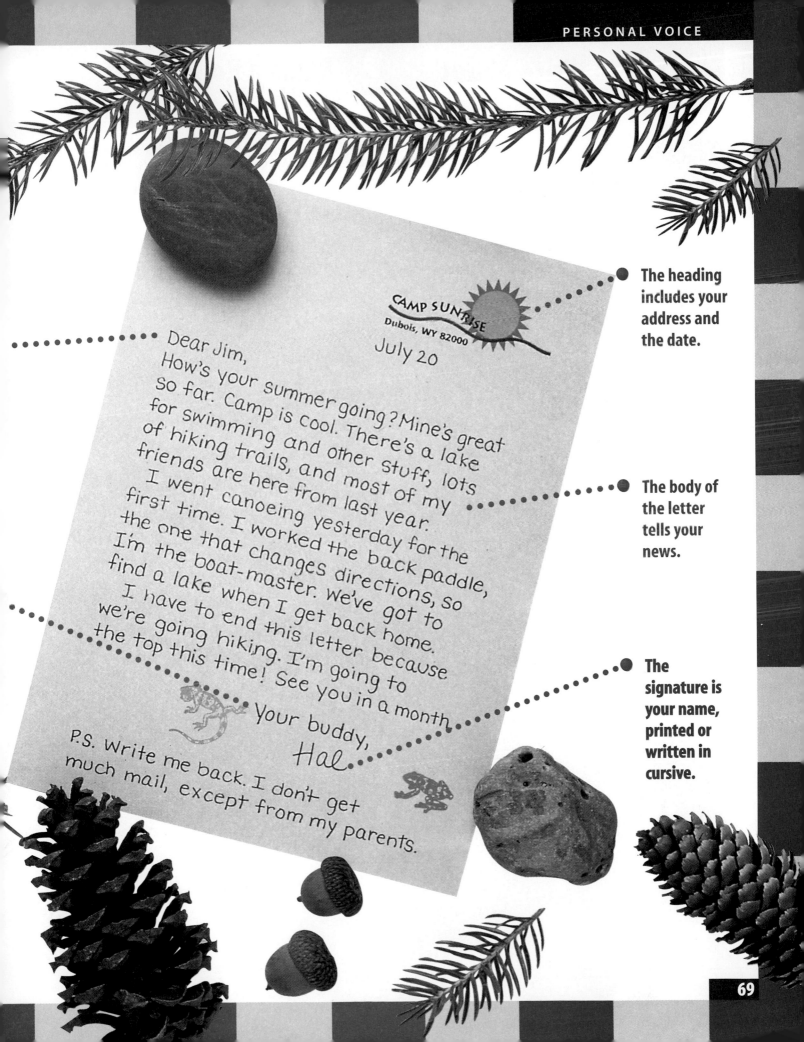

CAMP SUNRISE
Dubois, WY 82000

July 20

Dear Jim,
How's your summer going? Mine's great so far. Camp is cool. There's a lake for swimming and other stuff, lots of hiking trails, and most of my friends are here from last year.
I went canoeing yesterday for the first time. I worked the back paddle, the one that changes directions, so I'm the boat-master. We've got to find a lake when I get back home.
I have to end this letter because we're going hiking. I'm going to the top this time! See you in a month.

Your buddy,
Hal

P.S. Write me back. I don't get much mail, except from my parents.

The heading includes your address and the date.

The body of the letter tells your news.

The signature is your name, printed or written in cursive.

1 What to Write About

Think of some things you have learned to do recently, or a job you have finished or done well. Maybe you learned to use a computer, or built a birdhouse, or wrote a funny poem. List some of your achievements. Choose one achievement to write about in a friendly letter.

TOOLS

- pencil and paper
- envelope

2 Make a Rough Draft

Decide who will receive your letter. Will it be a best friend who moved away? a classmate at school? a favorite relative? Then, make a rough draft of what you want to say and include the following:

- Describe your achievement. Was it hard to learn? How long did it take you to do?

- Tell why it is important to you.

Now go back and reread what you have written. Are your thoughts clear? Is there anything else you want to say? Make your corrections.

Tip Remember, a rough draft doesn't have to be perfect. You can go back and make changes after you have finished it.

3 Write the Letter

Now write the final version of your letter. Use your best handwriting. You want your friend or relative to be able to read it. Remember, this is a letter to someone you know well. Make it warm and friendly.

Does your letter have:

- the date and your address?
- a greeting?
- a closing?
- your signature?

4 Send Your Letter

If you wish, you can show your letter to your teacher and classmates. Share your achievement with them, too. Then, address an envelope for the letter and put a stamp on it. Mail your letter to your friend or relative. If you're lucky, you'll receive a reply.

If You Are Using a Computer ...

As you revise your letter, use the electronic thesaurus to help you find just the right words. Choose a letterhead you like to create your own personal stationery. Then, use E-mail to send your letter on-line.

low to get to the waterfall

N W E

Hal Wong

CAMP SUNRISE
Dubois, WY 82000

Jim Smith
1 Main Street
Anytown

Parking

To Cascade Link Trail

White Tail Pond

THINK

Most days are filled with achievements, big or small. What is one thing you have done well today?

Keith Jardine
Wilderness Guide ▶

We can meet new challenges.

I Can Do It

Spend an exciting summer with María as she finds out what it takes to be a gaucho.

Ride the rapids with wilderness guide Keith Jardine.

Discover how young Clyde Bulla makes his dream of becoming a writer come true. Then find out how to have writing published.

PROJECT

Write an anecdote about something you're proud of.

Did I ever tell you about...

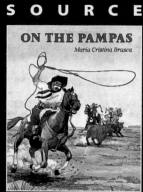

ON THE PAMPAS
María Cristina Brusca

ON THE PAMPAS

by María Cristina Brusca

74

I grew up in Argentina, in South America. I lived with my
family in the big city of Buenos Aires, but we spent our
summers in the country, at my grandparents' *estancia*. One
summer my parents and brother stayed in the city, so I
went without them.

My grandmother met me at the station in Buenos Aires,
and we had breakfast as we rode through miles and miles
of the flattest land in the world—the pampas. All around
us, as far as we could see, were fences, windmills, and
millions of cattle grazing.

Our station, San Enrique, was at the end of the line,
where the train tracks stopped. My grandfather was there
to meet us in his pickup truck and take us the five miles to
the estancia.

The ranch was called La Carlota, and the gates were
made of iron bars from a fort that had been on that very
spot a hundred years before. As we drove up to the gates,
we were greeted by a cloud of dust and a thundering of
hooves—it was my cousin Susanita, on her horse.

Susanita lived at the estancia all year round. She knew
everything about horses, cows, and all the other animals
that live on the pampas. Even though she was three years
younger than me, she had her own horse, La Baya.
Susanita was so tiny, she had to shimmy up La Baya's leg
to get on her back. But she rode so well that the gauchos
called her La Gauchita—"The Little Gaucho."

I didn't have a horse of my own, but old Salguero, the ranch foreman, brought me Pampita, a sweet-tempered mare, to ride. She wasn't very fast, but she certainly was my friend.

Susanita and I did everything together that summer. She was the one who showed me how to take care of the horses. We would brush their coats, trim their hooves, and braid their manes and tails.

Susanita was always ready for an adventure, no matter how scary. She used to swim in the creek holding on to La Baya's mane. At first I was afraid to follow her, but when she finally convinced me, it was a lot of fun.

I wanted to learn all the things a gaucho has to know. I wanted to ride out on the pampas every day, as Salguero did, and to wear a belt like his, with silver coins from all over the world and a buckle with my initials on it. Salguero said I'd have to begin at the beginning, and he spent hours showing Susanita and me how to use the lasso.

It was going to take a while for me to become a gaucho. The first time I lassoed a calf, it dragged me halfway across the corral. But Salguero told me that even he had been dragged plenty of times, so I kept trying, until I got pretty good at it.

Whenever the gauchos were working with the cattle, Susanita was there, and before long I was too. Sometimes the herd had to be rounded up and moved from one pasture to another. I loved galloping behind hundreds of cattle, yelling to make them run. I never got to yell like that in the city!

One day we separated the calves from the cows, to vaccinate them and brand them with "the scissors," La Carlota's mark. That was more difficult—and more

exciting, too. I tried to do what Salguero told me to, but sometimes I got lost in the middle of that sea of cattle.

At noon, everybody would sit down around one big table and eat together. I was always hungry. Grandma, Susanita's mother, and Maria the cook had been working hard all morning too. They would make soup, salad, and lamb stew or pot roast, or my favorite, *carbonada*, a thick stew made of corn and peaches.

After lunch the grown-ups took a *siesta*, but not us. We liked to stay outdoors. Some afternoons, when it was too hot to do anything else, we rode out to a eucalyptus grove that was nice and cool, and stayed there until it got dark, reading comic books or cowboy stories.

Other times we would gallop for two hours to the
general store and buy ourselves an orange soda. Then,
while we drank it, we'd look at all the saddles and bridles
we planned to have when we were grown up and rich.
Sometimes the storekeeper would take down a wonderful
gaucho belt like Salguero's, and we would admire the silver
coins and wonder where each one came from.

One day we rode far away from the house, to a field
where Susanita thought we might find *ñandú* eggs. They
are so huge, you can bake a whole cake with just one of
them. After riding around all afternoon, we found a nest,
well hidden in the tall grass, with about twenty pale-yellow
eggs as big as coconuts.

Salguero had warned us to watch out for the ñandú,
and he was right! The father ñandú, who protects the nest,
saw us taking an egg. He was furious and chased us out of
the field.

The next day we used the ñandú egg to bake a birthday
cake for my grandmother. We snuck into the kitchen while
she was taking her siesta, so it would be a surprise. The
cake had three layers, and in between them we put
whipped cream and peaches from the trees on the ranch.

We had a wonderful party for my grandmother's birthday.
The gauchos started the fire for the *asado* early in the evening,
and soon the smell of the slowly cooking meat filled the air.

There was music, and dancing, too. We stayed up
almost all night, and I learned to dance the *zamba*, taking
little steps and hops, and twirling my handkerchief.

Most evenings were much quieter. There was just the hum of the generator that made electricity for the house. We liked to go out to the *mate* house, where the gauchos spent their evenings.

We listened to them tell ghost stories and tall tales while they sat around the fire, passing the gourd and sipping mate through the silver straw. We didn't like the hot, bitter tea, but we loved being frightened by their spooky stories.

The summer was drawing to a close, and soon I would be returning to Buenos Aires. The night before I was to leave, Salguero showed me how to find the Southern Cross. The generator had been turned off, and there was only the soft sound of the peepers. We could see the horses sleeping far off in the field.

The next morning, my last at the estancia, Susanita and I got up before dawn. Pampita and the other horses were still out in the field. Salguero handed me his own horse's reins. He told me he thought I was ready to bring in the horses by myself. I wasn't sure I could do it, but Susanita encouraged me to try.

I remembered what I'd seen Salguero do. I tried to get
the leading mare, with her bell, to go toward the corral,
and the others would follow her. It wasn't easy. The foals
were frisky and kept running away. But I stayed behind
them until finally the little herd was all together, trotting in
front of me.

I was so busy trying to keep the foals from running off
that I didn't notice the whole household waiting in the
corral with Salguero. Everyone cheered as I rode in, and
before I knew it, my grandfather was helping me off the
horse. "You've become quite a gaucho this summer," he said.

My grandmother held out a wonderful gaucho belt like Salguero's, with silver coins from around the world—and my initials on the buckle!

"And," she added, "there's something else every gaucho needs. Next summer, when you come back, you'll have your very own horse waiting for you!" She pointed to the leading mare's foal, the friskiest and most beautiful of them all.

Before I could say a word, the foal pranced over to me, tossing his head. I would have the whole winter to decide what to name him, and to look forward to my next summer on the pampas.

MULITA

(moo-LEE-ta)
The mulita is a kind of armadillo. It spends the day in its burrow and comes out at night to look for food, mostly spiders and insects.

LAS PAMPAS

(las POM-pas)
The pampas are the very flat, almost treeless grasslands that stretch for hundreds of miles through central Argentina and Uruguay. Ranch animals live on the pampas year round, even during the mild winter months, eating grass.

HORNERO

(or-NAIR-oh)
The hornero is a kind of oven bird. Its nest looks something like an oven and is built out of clay, usually on top of a post or pole.

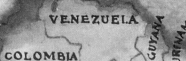

VENEZUELA
COLOMBIA
GUYANA
SURINAME
FRENCH GUIANA
ECUADOR
SOUTH AMERICA
PERÚ
BRAZIL
BOLIVIA
PARAGUAY
ARGENTINA
URUGUAY
THE PAMPAS
BUENOS AIRES
LA CARLOTA
SOUTH PACIFIC OCEAN
CHILE
SOUTH ATLANTIC OCEAN

REBENQUE

(ray-BAIN-kay)
A short, wide rawhide strap, used to lash cattle and horses.

LA CARLOTA'S BRAND

(la car-LOH-ta)
The brand represented two crossed fencing swords, but we called it "the scissors."

LECHUZA

(lay-CHOO-sa)
The lechuza, or burrowing owl, makes its home in holes abandoned by armadillos or other mammals. It likes to hunt in the evening.

YEGUA MADRINA

(YAY-goo-ah mah-DREE-na)
The yegua madrina, or leading mare of a herd of horses, keeps the herd together. She generally has a bell around her neck.

MATE
(MAH-tay)

Mate is a bitter, greenish tea. It is sipped through a silver straw called a bombilla (bome-BEE-yah) from a hollow gourd that is passed around.

ASADO
(ah-SAH-doh)

Meat, usually beef, roasted outdoors over a fire.

FACÓN
(fah-KONE)

A gaucho knife. Gauchos used to carry them as weapons, but now they are used for ranch work.

BOLEADORAS
(boh-lay-ah-DOOR-ahs)

Gauchos used to catch ñandús and other animals with boleadoras, which they threw in such a way that the animals' legs were tangled up in them.

GAUCHO CLOTHES

RASTRA
(RAH-stra)

A gaucho belt made from a wide strip of leather decorated with silver coins, usually from different countries. Some gauchos have their initials on the buckle.

BOMBACHA
(bome-BAH-cha)

Loose gaucho pants.

ÑANDÚ
(nyon-DOO)

The ñandú, or South American ostrich, is the largest bird in the Americas. It grows to be five feet tall and to weigh about fifty pounds. Although it cannot fly, it can run very fast. The male ñandú guards the nest, hatches the eggs, and takes care of the chicks.

RECADO
(ray-KAH-doh)

The gaucho saddle, made of many layers of leather and wool, with a sheepskin on the top.

ESTANCIA
(eh-STAHN-see-ah)

A South American cattle ranch.

91

Keith Jardine

Wilderness Guide

River rafting is **full of new** *experiences!*

Wilderness guide Keith Jardine works for a wilderness school. But his workplace isn't an indoor classroom. Instead, he grabs a paddle, puts on a life jacket, and jumps into a rubber raft. Jardine's job is taking adults and kids on adventure trips down some of California's fastest-moving rivers. And he loves every minute of it!

PROFILE

Name: Keith Jardine

Born: Sonoma, California

Job: wilderness guide

Hobby: river rafting

First wilderness experience: exploring his own backyard

Favorite wilderness place: California's Clavey River. He even named one of his sons Klavey, spelled with a *K*.

Fantasy adventure trip: rafting on a wild Alaskan river

HORIZON LINE

Recirculating Hole

Rock

Direction of Current

ALL ABOUT
Keith Jardine

Here's how wilderness guide **Keith Jardine** teaches **kids to meet adventure head on.**

"River rafting is a lot of fun," says Keith Jardine. "But it also takes a willingness to learn. You can't just jump in a boat and float down the river."

Jardine especially likes taking kids on raft trips. He finds that they are willing to listen and learn about the wilderness experience.

"Some kids already know a lot about the wilderness," says Jardine. "They're usually the ones who come from small towns and have spent time hiking or camping. But rafting is a different experience for city kids," he explains. "For many of them, the adventure is new and even scary."

What happens when kids are nervous about rafting? "I'm there to help them out," says Jardine. If kids are afraid to get into the raft, he tells them that they don't have to go. But he always asks them to give it a try. "By the time they're down the river a half mile, their attitudes usually change. They really start to enjoy it."

Jardine feels that wilderness adventures, on and off the river, can help kids find out about themselves. "They learn that it is okay to get out in the world and explore new things."

Exploring and looking for adventure have always been a part of Keith Jardine's life. As a kid he went hiking and camping with his parents. They taught him how to get along by himself in the woods. Meeting these challenges gave Jardine lots of self-confidence.

As a wilderness guide, Keith Jardine is still meeting challenges and learning about himself. And so are the kids who go rafting with him. A girl who was frightened about riding on the river discovered that she could help steer the big rubber raft. When she finished the trip, she said, "I can really do this!"

Keith Jardine thinks that new experiences like river rafting are good for kids. He says, "It's one of my goals to help these kids succeed. They can use that feeling of success in whatever else they do."

Keith Jardine's Tips for Meeting New Challenges

1. Learn all you can about what you're going to do. Ask questions.

2. Make sure you have all the gear or materials you need.

3. Tell yourself, "I can do this!"

4. Even if you're afraid, give it a try.

SOURCE

A GRAIN
OF WHEAT
A Writer Begins

CLYDE ROBERT BULLA

Autobiography

Clyde Robert Bulla as a child

From

A GRAIN OF WHEAT

A Writer Begins

by CLYDE ROBERT BULLA

Clyde Robert Bulla was born on a farm in Missouri on January 14, 1914. As a very young child, his favorite treasures were three books—Mother Goose, Peter Rabbit, and an ABC book. He spent hours looking at the pictures. But looking wasn't enough. Clyde wanted to go to school and learn to really read.

In first grade we had spelling, numbers, reading, and writing. I was slow at numbers, better at spelling. What I really liked were reading and writing. I wanted to learn new words. I wanted to write them and put them together to see what I could make them say.

I would write *apple*. It could be "*an* apple" or "*the* apple." It could be on a tree or in a dish. It could be green, red, or yellow.

A one-room schoolhouse very much like the one Clyde Bulla went to

Words were wonderful. By writing them and putting them together, I could make them say whatever I wanted them to say. It was a kind of magic.

Reading was a kind of magic, too. In a book I could meet other people and know what they were doing and feeling and thinking. From a book I could learn about life in other places. Or I could learn everyday things like tying a knot or building a birdhouse.

By the time I was ready for the third grade, I had read most of the books in our school library. There weren't many. I wanted more. Except for my three Christmas books, we had no children's books at home. I began reading whatever I could find in the family bookcase.

There was a thick book called *Oliver Twist*. It had words I didn't know, but there were many I *did* know, and I was able to read the story all the way through.

Lee, the soldier who married my sister, went to California. Louise followed him, but for a time she was in Missouri while he was far away by the Pacific Ocean. I wrote this poem about them:

California and Missouri

Hand in hand,
Over the sand,
Down by the sea,
And there sits Lee.
   'Tis California.

Go out and romp
In the swamp
And pick some peas.
There sits Louise.
   'Tis Missouri.

It was my first poem.

I started to write a story, but it was never finished. I called it "How Planets Were Born." This is the way it began: "One night old Mother Moon had a million babies. . . ."

Now I knew why I had said, in the first grade, that I wanted a table. Even then I wanted to be a writer. And didn't writers sit at tables or desks when they wrote?

I wanted to be a writer. I was sure of that.

"I'm going to write books," I said.

My mother said, "Castles in the air."

"What does that mean?" I asked.

"It means you're having daydreams," she said. "You'll dream of doing a lot of different things, but you probably won't do any of them. As you get older, you'll change."

I went from the second grade to the third to the fourth, and I hadn't changed. I still knew what I wanted to be.

I thought about writing and talked about it. I talked too much.

My father told me he was tired of listening to me.

"You can't be a writer," he said. "What do you know about people? What have you ever done? You don't have anything to write about."

In this little Missouri school, grades 1 through 8 all studied and learned in one large room—with one teacher!

When I thought over what he had said, it seemed to me he was right. I stopped writing. But not for long.

The city nearest us was St. Joseph, Missouri. Our newspaper came from there. In the paper I read about a contest for boys and girls—"Write the story of a grain of wheat in five hundred words or less." First prize was a hundred dollars. There were five second prizes of twenty dollars each. After that there were one hundred prizes of one dollar each.

I began to write my story. It went something like this: "I am a grain of wheat. I grew in a field where the sun shone and the rain fell."

I didn't tell anyone what I was doing. When my story was finished, I made a neat copy. I mailed it in our mailbox down the road.

A country mailbox like the one Clyde Bulla used to mail his story

Time went by. I began to look for the newspaper that would tell who had won the contest. At last it came.

There was a whole page about the contest. I saw I hadn't won the first prize. I hadn't won a second prize either. That was a disappointment. I had thought I might win one of the second prizes.

I read down the long list at the bottom of the page—the names and addresses of the boys and girls who had won the one-dollar prizes. Surely my name would be there. It *had* to be!

I read more and more slowly. Only a few names were left.

And one of them was mine! "Clyde Bulla, King City, Missouri."

"I won!" I shouted.

My mother looked at my name. "That's nice," she said.

Nice? Was that all she could say?

I started to show the paper to my father. There was something in his face that stopped me. I could see he wasn't happy that I had won a prize.

My sister Corrine was there. I could see she wasn't happy either. She was sorry for me because all I had won was a dollar.

Didn't they know it wasn't the dollar that mattered?

I had written a story that was all mine. No one had helped me. I had sent it off by myself. How many other boys and girls had sent their stories? Maybe a thousand or more. But my story had won a prize, and my name was here in the paper. I was a writer. No matter what anyone else might say, I was a writer.

from
THE INFORMATION PLEASE®
KIDS' ALMANAC

by
Alice Siegel & Margo McLoone Basta

CHILDREN AS AUTHORS

Many children have written books that have been published.
One of the first we know about is Francis Hawkins. In 1641,
when he was 8 years old, he wrote a book of manners for
children called *Youth Behavior*. Listed are other children
who have had their writing published. You may be able to
find their books in a library or bookstore.

• Dorothy Straight of Washington, D.C., was only 4 years
old when she wrote *How the World Began*. Her book was
published in 1964, two years later.

- A group of young Native American children in Arizona told their stories to their teacher, Byrd Baylor, who had them published in 1976 as *And It Is Still That Way.*
- When he was 9, David Klein wrote "Irwin the Sock" for a school assignment. The story of Irwin and Irina, matching argyle socks, was submitted to the Raintree Publish-A-Book Contest and won. It was published in 1988.

WHERE TO GET PUBLISHED

If you are interested in having your writing published, you can send your work to some of the publications listed below. Always enclose a stamped, self-addressed return envelope when sending material to any publication! Good luck!

Children's Digest, 1100 Waterway Blvd., Indianapolis, IN 46202. Publishes original fiction and nonfiction, poetry, and readers' favorite jokes and riddles.

Creative Kids, Prufrock Press, P.O. Box 8813, Waco, TX 76714. Gives children an opportunity to publish their work. Games, stories, and art for kids ages 8–14.

Jack and Jill, P.O. Box 567, Indianapolis, IN 46206. Publishes stories, poems, riddles, and jokes written by students in grades 2 through 6.

Stone Soup, The Magazine by Young Writers and Artists, P.O. Box 83, Santa Cruz, CA 95063. Publishes stories, plays, poems, and book reviews by children under 14.

WRITING CONTESTS

Publish-A-Book Contest
Winners of this contest will have their books published by Raintree Publishers. Writers in grades 2 through 6 can submit their stories to Raintree Publish-A-Book Contest, P.O. Box 27010, Austin, TX 78755.

How to
Write an Anecdote

Tell a **story about something** that *really* *happened* to **you**.

Suppose a friend says to you, "You'll never guess what I did last weekend." When you hear these words, you expect to hear an anecdote about your friend's experience. An anecdote is a short story about an interesting or funny event. Personal anecdotes are interesting to hear, but they are even more fun to share. And everyone has at least one.

Did I ever tell you about....

What's Your Story?

Think of something that has happened to you that would make a good story. It might be about something that surprised you.

It might be about something you didn't like and then learned to enjoy. It might even be about going to a new place or meeting new people. Jot down possible ideas. Then choose the one you like the most.

TOOLS

- paper and pencil

- colored pencils, crayons, or markers

...and when I looked around...

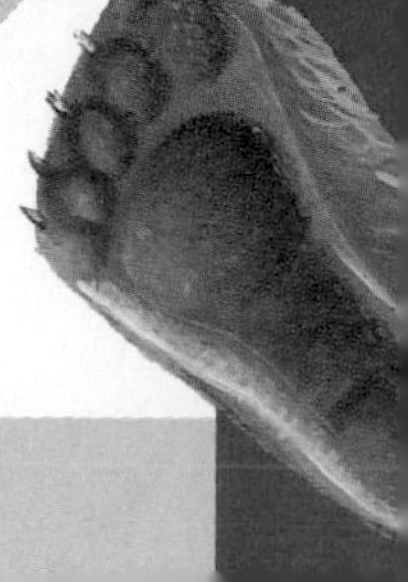

2 Get the Facts

Think about your anecdote. Try to get all the facts straight. Then take notes about what happened. Make sure you know the order in which the events in your story took place.

Now go back and look at your notes. Decide which details in your story are most important or interesting. Did something surprising or funny happen to you? Did you find out something about yourself—what you can do or what you like to do? Now you have all the information you need to put your anecdote on paper.

How Am I Doing?

Before you write your anecdote, take a few minutes to answer these questions.

- Is my anecdote about something that happened to me?

- Do I remember the parts of the story that are important?

- Does my story have a good ending?

Use your notes to write your story. Start out by briefly telling where the story takes place. Then tell what happened. As you write, imagine you are telling your anecdote to a friend. Try to make it lively. After you've finished, write the title and your name at the top.

Now illustrate your anecdote. Choose the part that you think is most important, and draw it. For example, if you won a prize, show yourself holding the prize.

Tip Personal anecdotes are always told in the first person. This means that you use the pronoun *I* when you tell your story.

What an ADVENTURE

4 Tell Your Story

Everybody loves to hear a good anecdote. Read yours to the class. Use lots of expression in your voice. Try to make your story sound exciting, funny, or scary. Display your illustration, too. Answer any questions your classmates may have about your anecdote.

If You Are Using a Computer ...

Tell your anecdote using the Record and Playback Tools on the computer. You can listen to your story as you write it. You may want to share your anecdotes with friends on-line.

that was!

CONGRATULATIONS

You have learned how new experiences can change you. They can make you feel good about yourself, too.

Keith Jardine
Wilderness Guide ▶

Glossary

bri•dles (brīd′lz) *noun*
The straps, bits, and reins that fit over horses' heads and are used to guide the animals.
▲ **bridle**

buf•fa•loes (buf′ə lōz′) *noun*
Wild oxen of North America that have large, shaggy heads. Also known as bison.
▲ **buffalo**

cal•lig•ra•phy (kə lig′rə fē) *noun*
Fancy penmanship, or a kind of beautiful writing.

chaps (chaps) *noun*
Leather leg coverings that are worn over pants. Chaps are worn by cowhands to protect their legs from thorns.

chick•en•pox (chik′ən poks′) *noun*
An illness. Most people who have chickenpox have a fever and red, itchy bumps on their bodies.

chop•sticks (chop′stiks′) *noun*
A pair of small sticks used to lift food to the mouth. Chopsticks are used mostly in Asian countries. ▲ **chopstick**

buffalo

Word Study

Long ago, the name that Chinese people gave their wooden eating utensils sounded a little like **chopsticks** to English sailors. The name stuck and is still used today.

corral

com•pete
(kəm pēt´) *verb*
To take part in a contest. Miguel will *compete* against Thomas in the big race.

con•ta•gious
(kən tā´jəs) *adjective*
Easily spread from one person to another. I caught Judy's cold because the germs were *contagious*.

cor•ral (kə ral´) *noun*
A place to fence in large animals, especially horses or cows.

course (kôrs) *noun*
An area for racing or other sport. The race *course* is behind the school.

court (kôrt) *noun*
A place marked off for playing certain games and sports. Tom is practicing his jump shot on the basketball *court*.

fin•ish line
(fin´ish līn´) *noun*
The place where a race ends. The frog hopped over the *finish line* and won the race.

gau•chos
(gou´chōz) *noun*
Cowhands from South America who work on the pampas. ▲ **gaucho**

Gi•la mon•sters
(hē´lə mon´stərz) *noun*
Large, poisonous lizards that live in the southwestern part of the United States and in Mexico.
▲ **Gila monster**

Gila monster

graz•ing
(grā´zing) *verb*
Feeding on growing grass or other plants. You might see animals like cows or sheep *grazing*.
▲ **graze**

hard•cov•er
(härd´kuv´ər) *adjective*
Having a cover that is stiff and sometimes covered in cloth. I bought a *hardcover* book about insects.

horned toads
(hôrnd´ tōdz´) *noun*
Small reptiles with short tails and spines that look like horns. Horned toads are also called horned lizards. ▲ **horned toad**

a	add	o͝o	took	ə =
ā	ace	o͞o	pool	a in *above*
â	care	u	up	e in *sicken*
ä	palm	û	burn	i in *possible*
e	end	yo͞o	fuse	o in *melon*
ē	equal	oi	oil	u in *circus*
i	it	ou	pout	
ī	ice	ng	ring	
o	odd	th	thin	
ō	open	ŧh	this	
ô	order	zh	vision	

Glossary

in•flam•ma•tion
(in′flə mā′shən) *noun*
A swollen area in some part of the body that is hot, red, and sore. The splinter in her finger caused an *inflammation*.

las•so (las′ō) *noun*
A long rope with a loop at the end used to catch cattle or horses.

manes (mānz) *noun*
The long patches of hair that grow along or around the necks of horses. ▲ **mane**

mane

news•pa•per
(nōōz′pā′ pər) *noun*
A set of printed sheets of paper containing news. A newspaper may be published daily or weekly.

or•chid (ôr′kid) *noun*
A plant with colorful flowers that grows in warm, damp places.

orchid

pam•pas
(pam′pəz) *noun*
A Spanish word that describes areas that are flat, with lots of grass and few trees. They are found in South America, especially in Argentina. The *pampas* stretch for hundreds of miles.

pre•scrip•tion
(pri skrip′shən) *noun*
A medical doctor's written order for medicine. Dr. Jenkins wrote a *prescription* for cough syrup to help me get well.

pub•li•ca•tions
(pub′li kā′shəns) *noun*
Things that are printed and published. Books, magazines, and newspapers are all publications.

pub•lished
(pub′lisht) *verb*
Printed an article or other written work in a newspaper, book, or magazine. Tonya's story was *published* in the town newspaper.
▲ **publish**

scal•lion
(skal′yən) *noun*
Any onion that doesn't have a bulb; a green onion.

ses•a•me noo•dles
(ses′ə mē nōōd′ lz) *noun*
Flat strips of dough covered with a sauce made from sesame seeds.
▲ **sesame noodle**

soy sauce
(soi′sos′) *noun*
A dark, salty liquid made from soybeans. It is used as a flavoring in some Asian foods.

spurs (spûrs) *noun*
Pointed metal pieces worn on the heels of boots that are used to poke a horse to make it move forward.

stam•pedes
(sstam pèds′) *noun*
Sudden rushes of herds of animals moving together. ▲ **stampede**

steth•o•scope
(steth′ə skōp) *noun*
An instrument used by doctors to listen to a person's heartbeat or breathing.

Word History

Stethoscope comes from two Greek words meaning "chest" and "examine." Today doctors often use **stethoscopes** to listen to, or examine, people's chests.

sub•mit•ted
(səb mit′ əd) *verb*
Sent written work to a newspaper, magazine, or book publisher in hopes of having it printed.
▲ **submit**

wheel•chair
(hwēl′chār) *noun*
A chair on wheels that a sick or injured person uses for moving around.

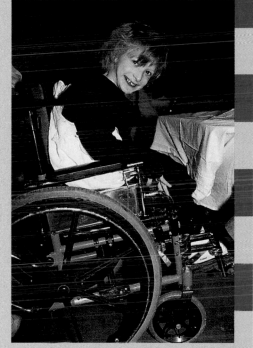

wheelchair

stethoscope

a	add	ŏŏ	took	ə =		
ā	ace	ōō	pool	ə in *above*		
â	care	u	up	e in *sicken*		
ä	palm	û	burn	i in *possible*		
e	end	yōō	fuse	o in *melon*		
ē	equal	oi	oil	u in *circus*		
i	it	ou	pout			
ī	ice	ng	ring			
o	odd	th	thin			
ō	open	th	this			
ô	order	zh	vision			

Authors & Illustrators

Gwendolyn Brooks *page 21*
Gwendolyn Brooks is one of the best-known poets in America. Although most of her poetry is written for adults, she wrote *Bronzeville Boys and Girls* just for children. In this book, her poems bring to life a whole neighborhood full of boys and girls. The poem "Narcissa" is from this special book.

María Cristina Brusca *pages 74–91*
This author/illustrator's childhood was very much like the girl's in *On the Pampas*. María Cristina Brusca really visited her grandparents' ranch while on vacation and dreamed of becoming a gaucho! Today, María Cristina Brusca lives and works in Kingston, New York. When she needs a break from working on a new book, she takes off on horseback and rides through the hills near her home.

Beverly Cleary *pages 22–35*

Since she was young, books have been important to Beverly Cleary and her family. Her mother opened the first lending library in the town where she was born. Beverly Cleary couldn't wait to learn how to read. But she was disappointed that the books she read were so unlike her own life. "I wanted to read funny stories about the sort of children I knew, and I decided that someday when I grew up I would write them." And she did. Today, children all over the world read Beverly Cleary's books.

"When you read, good things happen. Your life becomes more interesting and so do you . . . Read all kinds of books and welcome the world."

Dolores Johnson *pages 54–67*

Dolores Johnson says she hasn't been a kid in "a thousand years." But she can still remember what it was like to leave home for school for the first time, or the first time she was left with a babysitter. Dolores Johnson hopes that through her writing and artwork she can help kids find comfort and humor.

Marjorie Weinman Sharmat *pages 10–19*

This author decided at a very young age that she wanted to be a writer…or a detective or a lion tamer! When she was eight, she and a friend wrote a newspaper called *The Snoopers Gazette*. Marjorie Weinman Sharmat thinks that four people read it—her parents and her friend's parents. Now, thousands of people read her books—and she has written a lot: more than 110!

Books &

Author/Illustrator Study

More by Dolores Johnson

The Best Bug to Be
Kelly can't wait to be in the class play—until she finds out that she's not the star. She's supposed to play a bumble bee!

Pappa's Stories
Pappa's stories never sound like anyone else's. What's his secret?

What Kind of a Baby-sitter Is This?
Kevin is concerned because he doesn't like baby-sitters. Then he meets Aunt Lorey, a baby-sitter who shares his love of baseball.

Fiction

Class Clown
by Johanna Hurwitz
In this funny book, Lucas Cott decides he's tired of being the class clown. Follow his adventures as he tries to be a perfect student.

Dumpling Soup
by Jama Kim Rattigan
illustrated by Lillian Hsu-Flanders
For the first time, Marisa gets to make dumplings for the special New Year's soup. But will they be as good as the ones that her aunties make?

My Buddy
by Audrey Osofsky
illustrated by Ted Rand
Meet Buddy, a real working dog. His job is to make life easier for a boy who gets around in a wheelchair.

Nonfiction

I'm New Here
by Bud Howlett
Jazmin has just moved from El Salvador to the United States. In this photo essay, she describes her experiences during her first week in a new school.

My Mama's Little Ranch on the Pampas
by María Cristina Brusca
María's mother now owns and manages a ranch, and María and her brother love living there.

To the Limit
by Jeffrey Crelinstein
Professional athletes show how exercise can strengthen both the body and the mind. The amazing photos and diagrams in this book make you feel as if you are part of the action.

Media

Videos

Molly's Pilgrim
BFA Films and Videos
A young Russian immigrant girl brings new meaning to her class's Thanksgiving project. (24 minutes)

Pecos Bill
Rabbit Ears
Baby Bill is raised by coyotes. As an adult, he goes back to living with people and is able to do amazing things. This animated version of the classic tall tale is narrated by Robin Williams. (30 minutes)

The Red Shoes
Family Home Entertainment
This African-American version of a fairy tale tells what happens when a girl moves away from her old neighborhood. (30 minutes)

Software

Kid Works
Davidson & Associates
(IBM, Tandy)
The designers of this program call it "the creativity kit that writes, paints, and talks." This software makes it easy to tell and illustrate stories from your own life.

Super Munchers
MECC
(IBM, Macintosh Plus)
This game lets you take part in an exciting adventure. You also find out what you know about health, famous people, geography, and a variety of other topics.

Magazines

Stone Soup
Children's Art Fund
Read stories, poems, personal anecdotes, and book reviews written by children from all over the world.

Super Science Red
Scholastic Inc.
Hands-on activities, great pictures, and articles will help you make your own discoveries about health, growth, and the world around you.

A Place to Write

American Greetings to the World, P.O. Box 20118, Minneapolis, MN 55420

Have you ever thought about writing to a pen pal? This organization can help you connect with a pen pal from another country.

Acknowledgments

Grateful acknowledgment is made to the following sources for permission to reprint from previously published material. The publisher has made diligent efforts to trace the ownership of all copyrighted material in this volume and believes that all necessary permissions have been secured. If any errors or omissions have inadvertently been made, proper corrections will gladly be made in future editions.

Cover: Alan Tiegreen.

Interior: "Gila Monsters Meet You at the Airport" from GILA MONSTERS MEET YOU AT THE AIRPORT by Marjorie Weinman Sharmat, with illustrations by Byron Barton. Text copyright © 1980 by Marjorie Weinman Sharmat. Illustrations copyright © 1980 by Byron Barton. This edition is reprinted by arrangement with Simon & Schuster Books for Young Readers, Simon & Schuster Children's Publishing Division.

"Moving" from THE BUTTERFLY JAR by Jeff Moss. Copyright © 1989 by Jeff Moss. Used by permission of Bantam Books, a division of Bantam Doubleday Dell Publishing Group, Inc. "A Year Later" by Mary Ann Hoberman, published in YELLOW BUTTER PURPLE JELLY RED JAM BLACK BREAD by Viking Press. Text copyright © 1981 by Mary Ann Hoberman. Reprinted by permission of Gina Maccoby Literary Agency. "Narcissa" from BRONZEVILLE BOYS AND GIRLS by Gwendolyn Brooks. Copyright © 1956 by Gwendolyn Brooks Blakely. Reprinted by permission of HarperCollins Publishers.

"Another Big Event" and cover from RAMONA FOREVER by Beverly Cleary. Text copyright © 1984 by Beverly Cleary. Reprinted by permission of Morrow Junior Books, a division of William Morrow & Company, Inc. Cover illustration copyright © 1993 by Dell Publishing, a division of Bantam Doubleday Dell Publishing Group, Inc. Reprinted by permission. The trademarks Dell® and Yearling® are registered in the U.S. Patent and Trademark Office.

Time line from MY BACKYARD HISTORY BOOK by David Weitzman. Copyright © 1975 by The Yolla Bolly Press. By permission of Little, Brown and Company.

"April Chen" and cover from HOW MY FAMILY LIVES IN AMERICA by Susan Kuklin. Copyright © 1992 by Susan Kuklin. Jacket photographs copyright © 1992 by Susan Kuklin. This edition is reprinted by arrangement with Simon & Schuster Books for Young Readers, Simon & Schuster Children's Publishing Division.

"Kids Speak Up to Save Native Languages" by Sarah Jane Brian, in *Scholastic News*, November 12, 1993. Copyright © 1993 by Scholastic Inc. Reprinted by permission.

"Your Dad Was Just Like You" from YOUR DAD WAS JUST LIKE YOU by Dolores Johnson. Text and illustrations copyright © 1993 by Dolores Johnson. This edition is reprinted by arrangement with Atheneum Books for Young Readers, Simon & Schuster Children's Publishing Division.

"A Letter from Camp or a Trip" from PUTTING IT IN WRITING by Steve Otfinoski. Copyright © 1993 by Scholastic Inc. Published by Scholastic Inc. Used by permission.

"On the Pampas" from ON THE PAMPAS by Maria Cristina Brusca. Copyright © 1991 by Maria Cristina Brusca. Reprinted by arrangement with Henry Holt and Co.

Excerpt and cover from A GRAIN OF WHEAT by Clyde Robert Bulla. Copyright © 1985 by Clyde Robert Bulla. Reprinted by permission of David R. Godine, Publisher, Inc.

Excerpt and cover from THE INFORMATION PLEASE® KIDS' ALMANAC. Copyright © 1992 by Alice Siegel and Margo McLoone Basta. Reprinted by permission of Houghton Mifflin Co. All rights reserved.

Cover from THE CHALK BOX KID by Clyde Robert Bulla, illustrated by Thomas B. Allen. Illustration copyright © 1987 by Thomas B. Allen. Published by Random House, Inc.

Cover from HANNAH by Gloria Whelan, illustrated by Leslie Bowman. Illustration copyright © 1993 by Leslie Bowman. Published by Alfred A. Knopf, Inc.

Cover from MUGGIE MAGGIE by Beverly Cleary, illustrated by Kay Life. Illustration copyright © 1990 by Kay Life. Published by William Morrow & Company, Inc.

Cover from UNCLE JED'S BARBER SHOP by Margaree King Mitchell, illustrated by James Ransome. Illustration copyright © 1993 by James Ransome. Published by Simon & Schuster Books for Young Readers, Simon & Schuster Children's Publishing Division.

Photography and Illustration Credits

Photos: © John Lei for Scholastic Inc. all Tool Box items unless otherwise noted. p. 2 cl, tl, bl: © Rich Miller for Scholastic Inc. pp. 2-3 backgound: © Eric Burge/Flashback for Scholastic Inc. p. 3 bl: © Eric Burge/Flashback for Scholastic Inc.; tc: © H. Richard Johnston, 1992/FPG International Corp. p. 4 c: © Ana Esperanza Nance for Scholastic Inc.; tc: © FPG International Corp. p. 5 c: © Ana Esperanza Nance for Scholastic Inc.; tc: © FPG International Corp. p. 6 c: © Rich Miller for Scholastic Inc.; tc: © FPG International Corp. p. 38 all: © Stanley Bach for Scholastic Inc. p. 39 br: © Rich Miller for Scholastic Inc. p. 50 c: © Allen Russell/Profiles West. p. 51 bl: © Stephen Trimble; tr: © Lawrence Migdale. p. 52 tc: © Allen Russell/Profiles West. pp. 68-69 c: © John Lei for Scholastic Inc. p. 70 bl: © Stanley Bach for Scholastic Inc.; br: © John Lei for Scholastic Inc. p. 71 bl: © John Lei for Scholastic Inc. br: © Rich Miller for Scholastic Inc. p. 92 tc: © Richard Parker/Photo Researchers Inc.; leaves: © H. Richard Johnston, 1992/FPG International Corp.; all others: © Eric Burge for Scholastic Inc. p. 93 c: © Rich Miller for Scholastic Inc.; bc: © Rich Miller for Scholastic Inc. p. 94 tr: © Eric Burge/Flashback for Scholastic Inc.; c: © Robert A. Isaacs/Photo Researchers, Inc. p. 94 bc: © Rich Miller for Scholastic Inc. p. 95 tc: © Rich Miller for Scholastic Inc.; cr: © Eric Burge/Flashback for Scholastic Inc. p. 96 c: © From A GRAIN OF WHEAT by Clyde Robert Bulla. Reprinted by permission of David R. Godine, Publisher, Inc. Copyright © 1985 by Clyde Robert Bulla. p. 98 tl: © St. Louis Mercantile Library. p. 100 bl: © St. Louis Mercantile Library. p. 101 bc: © Archive Photos. p. 107 bc: © Stanley Bach for Scholastic Inc. p. 108 bc: © Stanley Bach for Scholastic Inc. p. 109 tc: © John Lei for Scholastic Inc.; cr: © Stanley Bach for Scholastic Inc. p. 110 bc: © Stanley Bach for Scholastic Inc. p. 111 br: © Rich Miller for Scholastic Inc. p. 112 bl: © Tim Davis/Photo Researchers, Inc. p. 113 tl: © Larry Prosor/SuperStock; bl: © Joseph T. Collins and Suzanne L. Collins/Photo Researchers, Inc. p. 114 cl: © R. Michael Stuckey/Comstock, Inc.; bc: © Simon D. Pollard/Photo Researchers, Inc. p. 115 bl: © David Wagner/Phototake, Inc.; tr: © Harvey Finkle/Impact Visuals; c: © p. 116 cl: © UPI/Bettmann Newsphotos. p. 117 br: © Deborah Grisorio; tr: © Margaret Miller. p. 118 br: © Joseph Nettis/Photo Researchers, Inc. p. 119 br: © Stephen Ogilvy for Scholastic Inc.

Illustrations: pp. 8-9, 22-35, 40-41, 72-73: Alan Tiegreen. pp. 20-21: Tony Caldwell. p. 103 Elwood H. Smith.